Think Happy, Be Happy

A Pocket Guide to Yoga Coaching

Tina Mundelsee

Illustrations by Karen Abend

ISBN 978-1-7345658-8-1

TABLE OF CONTENTS

INTRODUCTION

You are a soul having a human experience.

Yoga reminds you of who you truly are and coaches you how to operate your instruments—body and mind—from within. When you know how to deal with your mind, it will stop attacking you and start working for you. With your mind working for you, you create your reality and determine how you want to experience this lifetime!

Through the study and practice of Yoga, you align your life energies with all of existence and are able to tap into higher frequencies of reality and intelligence. While you move your body through the Yoga Asana, you create space and expand. From this place of openness, you start to unravel your thinking patterns, the stories your mind has been telling you, and your perception of yourself and your life.

As your awareness is raised through the practice of Yoga, so will your ability to tune into and deeply connect with your true Self and all other life forms on earth and beyond. If you invite the science of Yoga into your life and open up fearlessly to all possibilities, you will leave your human struggles with I-ness behind and live your life as a blissful experience of One-ness.

We invite you to curiously experiment with your instruments, body and mind, and realize that the key to a fulfilling life and harmonious relationships lies within you. And while you silently witness your human experiences during your practice, you remember who you are, who we are, and what life is all about.

We are grateful to share this journey with you. It is our heartfelt intention to help you on the path to awakening to your full potential and the joyful life yo deserve!

EMBARK ON YOUR INNER JOURNEY

LOTUS

I embark on my inner journey and discover that everything I have been looking for is already inside of me. There is no void to fill. I am complete.

In this journey of life, I have manifested as a human being. The world is ever-changing, but I am not from this world. My true Self is unconditional wisdom, love, and bliss. I am a soul. I am divine energy. I am an actor in this divine play called life.

I do not identify with my role. I just play my role as best as I can while using the instruments of my body and mind. I joyfully accept the universe's script and trust that there are no mistakes.

When I lose my place in the script, I turn inwards and remember who I am—a soul.

OM
VIBRATE WITH THE SOUND OF YOUR TRUE NATURE
AUM
BIRTH → EXISTENCE → TRANSFORMATION
ACCEPT EMBRACE AND HONOR THE CIRCLE OF LIFE

Although it is written OM, this mantra has three parts when it is chanted: A-O-M, like Birth – Life – Transformation.

I close my eyes. I cover my ears with my hands. I hum the Mantra OM. I turn my focus inward to the sound of my true being. I feel the A reverberating below my navel, the O in my rib cage, and the M in my throat.

While I observe how life plays its melody, I am not disturbed by the sound. I am fully present in my unchanging frequency of OM.

All of creation is animated by the same divine energy and the vibrating sound of this energy is the Mantra OM. I am OM.

While this body and mind undergo the circle of life, like a dancer moving to different melodies and rhythms, I am the underlying, unchanging sound of OM.

I joyfully accept the changes my body and mind undergo in the circle of life. I dance to every melody while my own true frequency is the unchanging sound of OM.

MALASANA

DON'T REACT

ACT CONSCIOUSLY

My thoughts, words, and actions have consequences. During every moment of my human experience, I own my power to make a choice. I choose how to respond to life events.

Before I think, speak, or act, I stop for a moment. I breathe and ask myself:

Is my choice of thought, speech, or action harming myself or someone else by satisfying my Ego and merely creating a fleeting moment of joy? Or does it contribute to my ultimate goal of long-lasting inner peace and balance?

I am conscious that my thoughts, words, and actions determine the quality of my life.

12 1

11 2

MOVE WITH
EASE THROUGH
THE UPS AND
DOWNS OF LIFE

10 3

9 4

8 5

7 6

My mind judges and labels life events according to its content, values, and beliefs. Until I take my power back from my mind, my mood will always be dependent on life circumstances. I have the power to tell my mind to change its perception, shift its focus, give a different meaning to life events, or simply have faith that nothing in the universe is going wrong.

It is my responsibility to create a pleasant atmosphere in my mind. The content of my mind works as a filter through which I perceive life. If my mind is full of darkness, life seems miserable. If its contents are pleasant, life is a miracle. When negative thoughts arise, I turn them around, think of the opposite and create a positive affirmation that I repeat to myself.

I joyfully observe my mind's roller coaster ride of emotions while I remember who I am.

My true state of being is equanimity. I am divine energy—a soul animating this human being. While this human being is subject to suffering and joy, I am unconditional bliss.

The divine manifests in miraculous ways and in an infinite number of shapes, forms, and energy waves.

My human eye perceives each form as a separate being, and my human mind perceives each circumstance as a separate life event. My Ego only sees differences, but the "I" that is my Higher Self knows that differences appear only to the human mind. I see beyond and perceive the interconnectedness of all life.

We are all one. We are all just little drops in the vast ocean of existence. We are all experiencing life in different forms, but there are no differences. Each life form, from the smallest atom to the tallest tree is the same and shares the same desire. We all want peace.

Because I see no differences, I have no fear. I sense no competition. I do not judge myself or others. I do not feel jealousy, anger, or shame. I just am—a small drop of the ocean of existence trying to find its way back home.

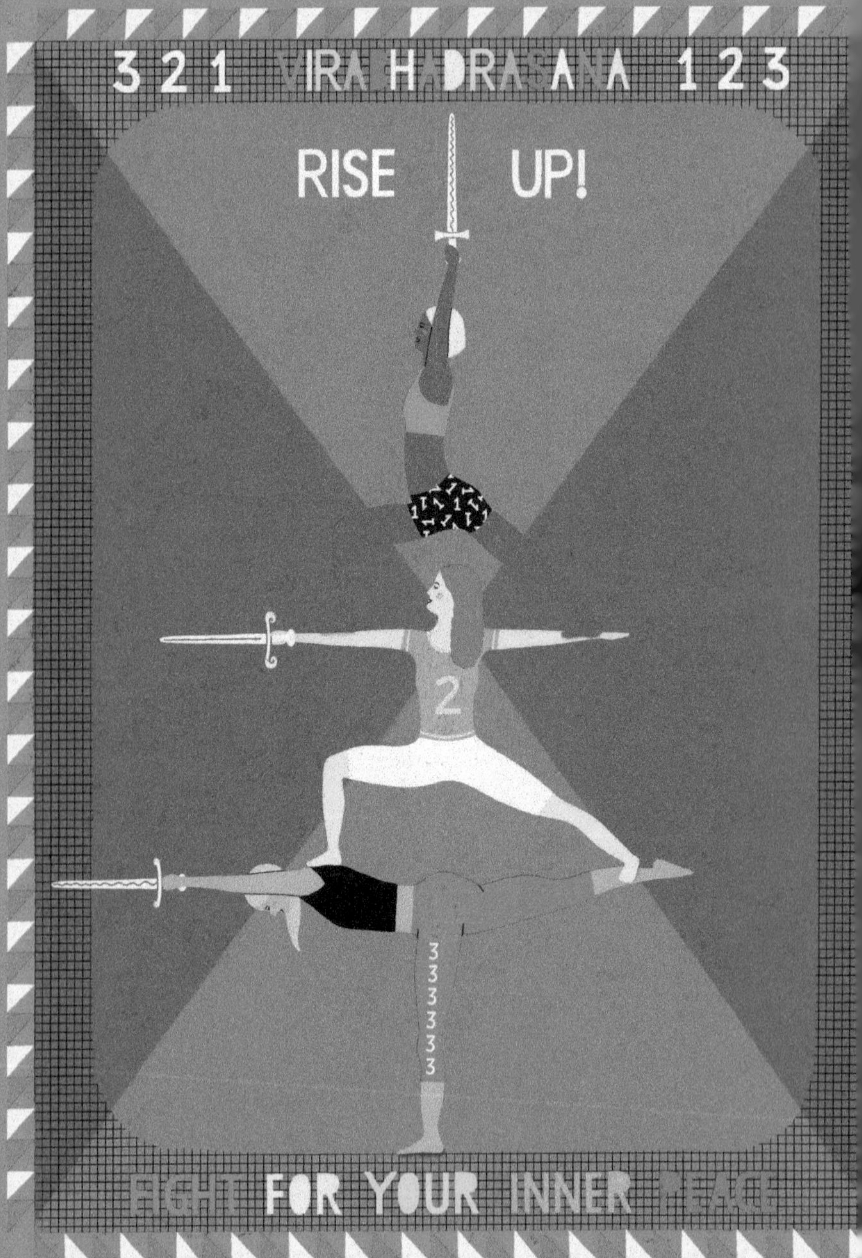

3 2 1 VIRABHADRASANA 1 2 3
RISE UP!
2
FIGHT FOR YOUR INNER PEACE

When my mind gets off balance for any reason—because of a thought, because of my mind's own negative self-talk or self-criticism, because of a memory, a worry, a fear, a habit, a relationship, physical pain, a word someone said, a gesture someone made, or any external circumstance—I know I have given my power away.

I imagine my power to be like the anchor of my vessel that accidentally got tangled in one of the above, pulling me away from my destination of "peace" and holding me back from sailing joyfully through life.

I haul my anchor in. I take my power back.

In every moment of my human experience, I have the power to choose to be at peace. I am the captain of my vessel. I am the soul in my body and mind.

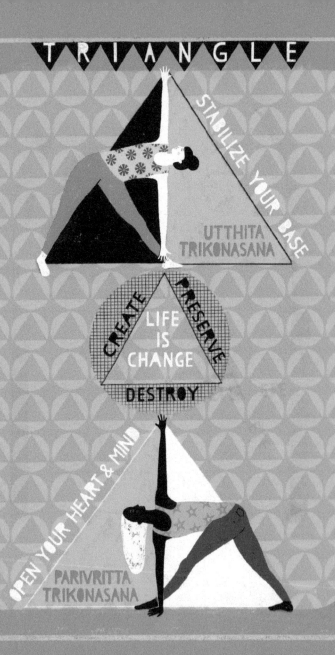

My beliefs and values create the base from which my thoughts emerge. My thoughts create my emotions. My emotions motivate my actions. My actions determine the quality of my life.

I cannot continue believing, thinking, saying, and doing the same things and expect different results.

Personal evolution requires a change in my habitual behavioral patterns and belief systems. I am ready to move out of my comfort zone to create positive change.

I am not afraid of change. I am not afraid of letting go of my old beliefs about myself and about how life is supposed to be. I have the power to believe in anything I want. My beliefs become my reality.

Starting now, I believe that I AM ENOUGH. Everything is AVAILABLE TO ME.

UTTHITA

EXPAND

BEYOND

YOUR

COMFORT

ZONE

TO

CREATE

CHANGE

PARSVAKONASANA

I am flexible. I am able to adapt while respecting my feelings and the boundaries I set for myself.

I can expand my mind beyond its limiting beliefs. I am the power to create change. I courageously move out of my mind's comfort zone and from the known into the unknown. I cannot fail, but instead gain experience and learn from the lessons of life. I am not afraid to fall because I have the power to pull myself up an infinite number of times. I govern my mind and do not allow for self-doubt or procrastination.

My life is an infinite source of possibilities. My mind cannot stop me or hold me back from experiencing life joyfully!

PARSVOTTANASANA

BOW DOWN

HUMBLY AND

FREE YOURSELF

FROM THE

PRISON OF

YOUR MIND

Everything that limits my joyful experience of life is a creation of my human mind.

As long as I mistakenly identify myself with this body and the content of this mind, my inner peace and happiness will be dependent on my mind.

I am not who my mind wants me to believe I am. I am not my story. I am not my past. I am not my worries. I am not my limiting beliefs. I am not a prisoner of my mind. I am not the mind. I am the master of my mind.

I am free because I remember who I truly am—a soul, having a human experience, equipped with a body and a mind. I am unconditional peace and bliss. I am not subject to change, time, thoughts, feelings, emotions, or life events. I have always been; I will always be. I am just that—pure existence —the source of creation.

My parents are my roots. I am grateful they gave me the gift of life and the opportunity to have a human experience.

They did their best, even though their best was not always enough for me. They made mistakes because they did not know how to do it differently. They are just human beings and have their own emotional baggage to carry.

I do not have to agree with my parents, but I accept them because they are a part of me. Only when I accept my parents, my roots, am I able to fully love and accept myself.

I no longer need to please my parents to feel loved and accepted, nor do I need their approval. I am free and stand fully in my power.

I am setting healthy boundaries with my parents and mutually respect their own boundaries. I am able to say no when I want to say no and yes when I want to say yes without any feeling of guilt.

I am a grown up. My roots are healed. I use my life lessons, whether they are pleasant or painful, to create the life I want. Nothing from my past is holding me back. Everything is available to me. Life is NOW.

NATARAJASANA

BURN YOUR DEMONS

DANCE WITH THE FLAMES OF LIFE

I let go of all false ideas about myself. I let go of what I believe to be my story. I let go of my limiting beliefs, worries, and fears.

Write down the limiting beliefs you have about yourself. Write down your self-doubts. Write down the stories you are attached to. Then, when you feel ready, light that piece of paper on fire and let it burn!

As the paper transforms into ash, my self-doubts transform into self-love and empowering beliefs about myself.

I am free. I dance on the waves of life with joy, balance, and divine bliss!

When you feel anxious or sad, it means your energy has become hooked into limiting beliefs like stories, worries, or other people's feelings or judgements. Visualize yourself like a fisherman who takes his hook out of every unnecessary thing caught on his fishing line and reels it back in. You energetically unhook from anything that causes you pain. You reel in your power and visualize yourself within an impermeable wall of healing white light. This is your energetic boundary. Here you are safe and protected. Always.

I focus steadily on my burning desire for unconditional love, peace, and bliss until it becomes reality. Until I remember my divine identity.

I commit to my purpose in life. I commit to my relationships. I commit to my goals. I avoid any thoughts, words, or behaviors that do not contribute to these commitments and my highest intention.

Train your mind to maintain its focus on pleasant thoughts and your highest intention. Practice daily to keep your uninterrupted focus on your breath for three minutes. When your mind wanders off or you get caught in a dialogue with your thoughts, just bring your focus back to your breath.

Your mind is like a muscle. Through practice you will succeed and probably very soon will want to stay there for much longer than just three minutes.

LET YOUR THOUGHTS JUST PASS BY

LISTEN TO YOUR INTUITION NOT YOUR MIND

YOU KNOW WHAT TO DO

TRUST YOURSELF

UTTANASANA

I no longer believe everything my mind says, take every thought seriously, or allow any kind of self-criticism. Instead, I love myself and connect with my heart and intuition. Only if I love and respect myself can others love me in return. I am the only one who knows exactly what I need. I hear myself. I am kind to myself. I allow myself to enjoy the experience of life.

I trust myself completely. I hear my true voice beyond the chatter of my mind. I carry all of the answers inside of me. I am the all-knowing soul.

Close your eyes, turn your focus inwards, focus on the point between your eyebrows, let your breath flow freely through your being. Dive into the silent space between two thoughts and just listen.

YOU ARE NOT A VICTIM OF YOUR PAST...

BADDHA KONASANA

...BE FREE...

My past has long passed; that is why it is called "The Past". Whatever happened in the past did not happen because of me; it did not happen TO me. Life just happens. My past is not MY story, it is THE story of life. It is not my task to understand WHY things happened, I just have to humbly accept that the Universe does not make mistakes. Nothing went wrong.

I am not a victim of my past. I am a survivor of my past.

I am no victim. I am a student of life and I draw from every lesson learned.

The unwavering belief that nothing wrong ever happens is my gateway to ultimate freedom from suffering. I joyfully accept whatever life offers me.

FORGIVENESS

IS THE KEY TO

LIBERATION

Every person does his or her best in every moment of life. Sometimes my best was not enough, but I did what felt right in that moment. I did what I had to do. I stand by my choices. I forgive myself and do not dwell on feelings of guilt or shame. Human beings make mistakes; that is how we are designed.

Nothing from my past can stop me from moving on, shining my light, and living my life joyfully. I forgive myself. I forgive others who hurt me and I ask for forgiveness in return so that I can break out of the prison of my mind.

I am not wasting any more time on my mind's self-doubts, should haves and would haves. Only by forgiving myself am I able to forgive others and to be forgiven.

Write a letter to a person who hurt you or was hurt by you and express your heartfelt feelings. Liberate your heart, let your tears flow freely and finally let go. You do not have to actually send your letter, but keep it as a reminder of your power to set yourself free.

PASCHIMOTTANASANA

INHALE
TO
REACH
BEYOND
THE
PAST

EXHALE
TO
EMBRACE
THE
MAGIC
OF
LIFE
NOW

I take my power back and use my memory only when it serves me. I am the master of my mind. Life is happening NOW.

I am here now. My life is now. Every breath is happening only now. The now is the only truth. I am living only now. The past has passed and the future is only an imagination.

I am not wasting any more precious time dwelling on the past and missing the magic of life now.

My life is too precious to spend time worrying about the things I cannot control or change, like the past, the future, or other people's behavior.

Once a day, stop. Take life in with all five senses. Do not judge, name, or label anything you experience. It is just that. It is as it is and that is okay. All is well.

When your mind tries to pull you into the past, connect with your breath. Your breath is your anchor in the now and your reminder that the present moment is the only truth.

THE LOVE

YOU SEEK IS ALREADY

IN YOU

My physical appearance and my mind feel separate and incomplete. Therefore, my mind seeks completion in others. My mind, my wrong identity, my Ego, expects others to save me from my sufferings and to bring me the happiness I long for. Expectations lead to delusions and cannot be the basis for any harmonious relationship.

Instead, my true Self, the soul, is in perfect balance—male and female, yin and yang, sun and moon. Nothing is missing. I am complete. I joyfully observe my longings for salvation and my attachment to my body and mind. I consciously and joyfully decide to satisfy my needs without expectations. Relationships based on expectations only bring delusion and suffering.

I have to first love myself in order to love others and to allow others to love me.

'You shall love your neighbor AS YOURSELF.' There is no other commandment greater than these." Bible, Mark 12:31

In any relationship, I respect the necessary boundaries to stay true to myself, my feelings, and my values.

I am pure love. My light vibrates in every cell of my body and mind. The love I seek is already in me. I am in love with life.

When you wake up in the morning, look in the mirror, hug yourself and tell yourself kindheartedly: I love you. You are enough.

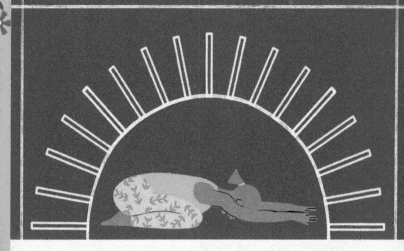

CLEAR YOUR SLATE EACH DAY AND FEEL NEWBORN

When I feel frustrated, unheard, mistreated, fearful, or just sad, my inner child is present. I imagine talking like a nurturing mother to the little version of myself who is having a meltdown. Only I am able to completely understand myself. Only I know how to calm down my inner child. I hold myself lovingly and tell myself that all will be well.

In a challenging moment, hug yourself and tell your inner child exactly what it needs to hear to feel loved, to feel safe, to feel enough.

Observe the challenging emotions; calm yourself down and let them go. Do not hold onto negative feelings. They will grow into bigger energetic obstacles and manifest as physical tensions or mental imbalances.

With every breath, I am a newborn. I clear my slate. I start afresh and move through life joyfully without any emotional pain or suffering.

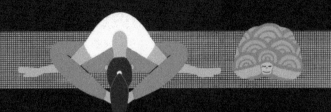

PULL YOUR SENSES INWARD

TO DISCOVER YOUR TRUE INNER SELF

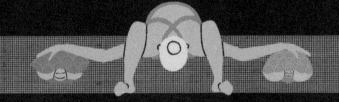

Beyond this physical body lies a field of energy. All of life is energy, interconnected and in constant communication. When I take in and accumulate negative energy, I am thrown off balance. This energetic imbalance is experienced as negative thoughts in my mind or as physical sufferings in my body.

When you notice a physical or mental imbalance like pain, skin irritations, tension, sleeping disorders, anxiety, or depression, gently slide your hand over your whole body and try to detect where this feeling, imbalance, or energy block is located in your energetic body.

Wherever your hand wants to stop, keep it there. Feel into that space. Listen to that space. Do you feel energy spinning there? Do you feel heaviness? Do you feel any energetic congestion?

Now, with loving kindness, start rubbing this place. Gently move your hand in a circular motion on the spot with the intention to loosen energetic knots or blocks and liberate negative energies. This will allow your energy to flow freely and evenly in your whole being and give you a sense of total balance.

When I tune into my energy body with my highest intention to heal, I can truly change my life physically, mentally, emotionally, and spiritually.

It is as simple as adjusting my antenna from picking up disturbing noise to receiving the frequency of peace and joy and feeling at ease with that change.

My body is made to heal itself physically and emotionally.

I am able to heal myself.

ARDHA

WHEN YOU FORGIVE AND ASK FORGIVENESS PAIN AND ANGER LEAVE YOUR BODY

MATSYENDRASANA

The nature of life is change. When I hold on for too long to the same beliefs about myself, about how others should treat me, and how life should be, I find myself stuck in limitations. I end up carrying around the same old emotional baggage and personal development becomes impossible.

My beliefs become my reality. Be careful what you tell yourself. Your brain believes everything you say and tries to give you exactly what you ask for.

I have the power to change. By giving a different meaning to life events, I change the emotion I have about it. Changing my beliefs about myself opens the door to infinite possibilities.

Whatever change you desire, phrase it in the present tense, as if it were already true. Repeat it constantly with love, passion, and your highest intention. The energy you send out will attract what is similar and manifest in your life. What you send out into the universe comes back to you.

My relationships are harmonious and brighten my life. I am greeted by love everywhere I go. I am lovable and treated with love and respect. I am an infinite source of love.

My relationship with myself is the longest relationship I will ever have. I love myself exactly as I am.

BHARADVAJASANA

TURN AWAY FROM YOUR NEGATIVE THOUGHTS

I am the creator of my emotions. My body posture influences my emotions. The language I use to talk to myself and others influences my emotions. But mostly the thoughts I focus on determine how I feel.

My focus and attention are the nourishment for my thoughts. If I think about the opposite or simply turn away from unpleasant and unnecessary thoughts, negative self-talk, resentment, pain, complaints and inner resistance, they will simply wither and die.

Where your attention goes, your emotions go. Where your emotions go, your actions go. Where your actions go, your destiny goes.

Practice maintaining your attention with this simple exercise and you will be able to keep your attention on pleasant thoughts:

One at a time, simply bring your fingers down to touch the tip of your thumb. Start according to these directions: Touch your index finger to your thumb, then touch your middle finger, your ring finger, and last, your pinkie finger to your thumb. Then go back ring finger to thumb, middle finger, index finger, and start over again. Keep going as fast as you want and repeat as often as you want.

Since each fingertip represents one of the 5 elements you also create an energetic balance in your body with this exercise which results in a state of mental ease.

LET GO OF YOUR BAGGAGE AND FLY HIGH

By giving love and appreciation to myself and others, I uplift myself.

We all have the same needs and our desire to satisfy our needs motivates our actions. When we understand the needs of another person, we understand why they do what they do. When all our needs are satisfied, we feel in balance and fulfilled.

Which of the following needs are a priority in your life, your relationships, and your career? Are you satisfying your needs in a healthy and joyful way? Which needs lack your attention? Tony Robbins identifies six human needs:

- Certainty – the assurance to avoid pain and gain pleasure
- Uncertainty – variety, going into the unknown and looking for change
- Significance – feeling heard, needed, special, and appreciated
- Connection/Love – connection with myself and others, self-love, to love and be loved
- Growth – personal development, progress, the need to develop and expand
- Contribution – the need to give beyond yourself, a sense of service and focus on supporting, helping, and giving to others

I am taking good care of myself and give myself what I need.

STOP BLAMING

SO YOU CAN

OPEN UP

TO LOVE

I am letting go of my fear of being unlovable. Nothing can hold me back from experiencing the infinite magic that life and relationships have to offer.

Only when I fully forgive, respect, and love myself am I allowing others to forgive, respect, and love me.

Feelings of blame, shame, fear, and resentment keep us contracted, tense and small, obstructing our natural flow of vital energy. When our energy gets out of balance, we feel mental imbalances like anxiety or depression. Mental imbalances create physical imbalances, which manifest as physical disease or tension in our body.

Feelings of gratitude and loving kindness expand our energy field, clear our energetic pathways, and create harmony in our being.

Make a gratitude jar. Every day put a little note in it with at least one thing you have been grateful for today. On difficult days, when you are contracted and have a feeling of unease, read the notes you have put into your jar to help you reclaim your harmonious balance.

I am kind and lovable.

DHANURASANA

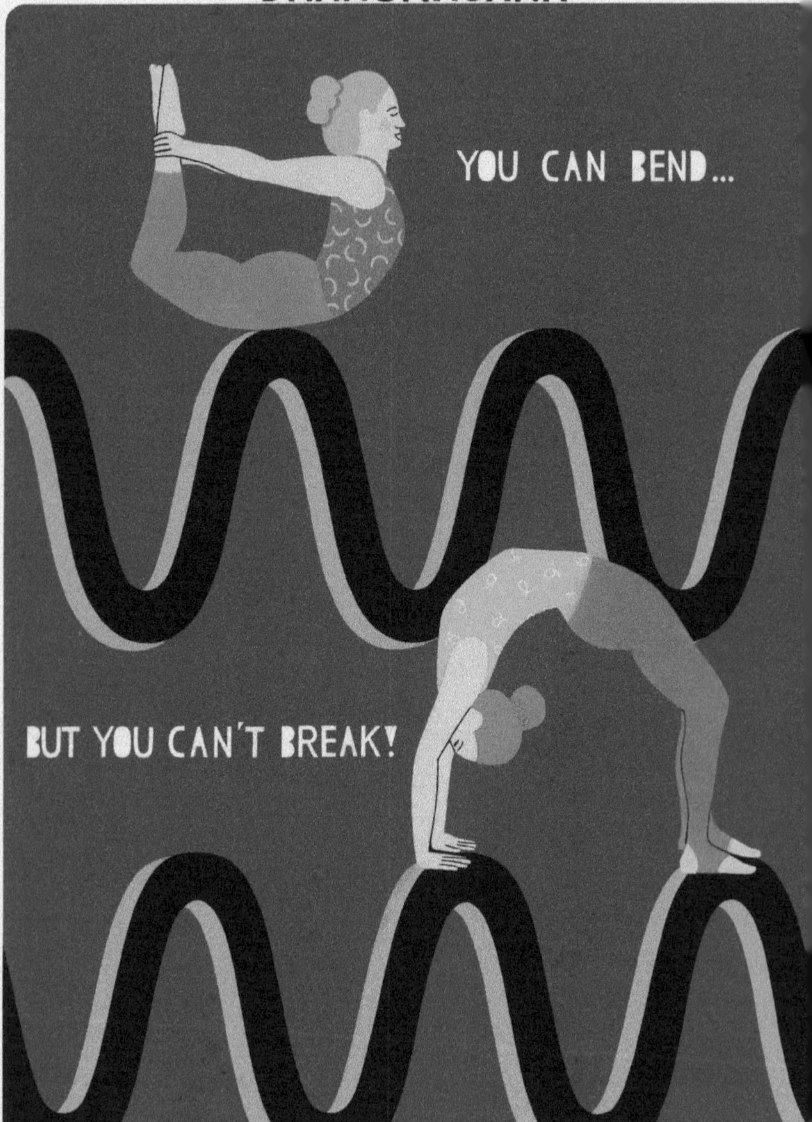

URDHVA DHANURASANA

I am flexible and able to adapt to life's circumstances joyfully.

I am grateful for being myself. I stop comparing myself to others and instead stand in my own power. I believe in myself. I am doing my best and shine my unique light onto others. I am contributing with my joyful being to the happiness of others.

Take a social media break sometimes. It is easy to fall into a habit of comparing yourself to others and focusing only on what is missing. Who do YOU really want to be? What do YOU like? What are YOUR gifts? You are unique and there will always be someone out there who needs your light and needs to hear exactly what you have to say.

Whatever you do, just do it for the pure love of doing it. Act with love and without expectations. Expectations are the root cause for delusion and disappointment.

Make sure that your thoughts, words, and actions are in harmony.

I have no expectations. I am just doing my best and let the universe take care of the rest. I surrender my efforts and actions humbly to a higher force without expecting anything in return.

HEROS
DON'T
FIGHT

THEY LET GO
AND SURRENDER

I am not judging myself and I am not judging others. I free myself and stop caring what other people think of me. I am enough.

I am not afraid of being vulnerable.

Vulnerability is empowering because it makes us creative. It frees us from old restrictions and helps us see new possibilities. When we notice a weakness and acknowledge it, we get a chance to find ways to overcome it.

Letting down my guard is a commitment to my growth.

I am not hiding behind the walls of my created identity any longer, and instead open up to others and allow them to love me for who I truly am.

Make your right hand into a fist and with a steady rhythm pound on your chest like a gorilla. Imagine that with your energy you are breaking down the walls you have built around your heart, while inviting in courage and self-esteem.

SHALAMBA

FIND UNITY
BEYOND DUALITY

SARVANGASANA

I am moving from my head into my heart, the chamber of the soul, my true Self.

I change my perspective. I shift my view of myself and the world to fully embrace and enjoy every present moment of my life. I am not scared of turning my world upside down.

I am changing my limiting beliefs into empowering beliefs. I am letting go of old ideas about myself and how life is supposed to be. I courageously observe my conditioned mind and change what has to be changed to improve my life and the lives of others.

I have faith that the universe knows exactly what it is doing. I have faith that nothing ever goes wrong. As long as I believe that something is wrong and as long as I keep asking Why, I am living in resistance and disagreement with what is. This inner resistance will create energetic, mental, and, ultimately, physical imbalances.

My human mind is limited, conditioned, and unable to understand life's mysterious ways. I move beyond my mind's ideas of right and wrong. I do not have to understand why things happen. I just have to let them happen and joyfully accept the creator's divine script. I surrender. I have faith. I trust.

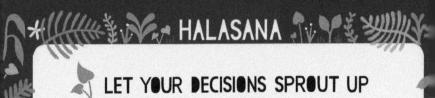

HALASANA

LET YOUR DECISIONS SPROUT UP

FROM A CLEAR MIND

AND AN OPEN HEART

In any given moment of my life, I choose my thoughts, words, and actions wisely, with my highest intention in mind—inner balance and peace.

Before making a big decision, ask yourself: Is my decision only based on egoistical needs? Am I hurting someone with my decision? What would X do in my position (think about a teacher or a virtuous person you look up to)? Is my decision based on facts, on my heartfelt desire, and my highest intent? Am I choosing the easy way out, or am I ready to move beyond my comfort zone? Is this decision based on the truth of what I really want, contributing to what I love and what I am passionate about?

Play out the results and consequences of your decision in your mind and see how it makes you feel. Pretend you are already there and experience the emotions it creates.

I am calling on my spirit guides, my ancestors, my animal guides, my fairy godmother, the stars and planets, mother moon, and father sun to send me the wisdom and knowledge I need to make the right decision.

Close your eyes, turn the volume of your mind's chatter down, just be, just listen, do not wait, and do not enter into a dialogue with your thoughts. Do not ask—just listen and make space. Be an empty container, ready to receive. Open all channels and allow yourself to receive guidance. It will come. It always does. Be patient.

I fully trust myself.

MATSYASANA
BREATHE OUT THE THOUGHTS
YOU DON'T NEED TO SAY
LET UNNECESSARY WORDS
AND EXPECTATIONS FLOAT AWAY

I allow myself to set healthy boundaries to protect my inner peace and to maintain harmony between what I think, feel, and do. Only with this inner balance am I able to contribute to the well beings of others.

I allow myself to say no to what does not align with my heart, and to say yes to what does. I am not afraid of disappointing others. I do not say yes just because it is hard to say no. Boundaries are necessary to stay balanced, healthy, and honest—to live a life that is true to me.

Give for the love of giving and without expecting a certain result, but make sure that some form of energy exchange is happening. That could just be an expression of gratitude, appreciation, a smile, a gesture, a kind word, a hug, or the sum of money required for a service. If you feel you are always giving without receiving an energetic exchange, you will be at risk of feeling burned out and exhausted.

When you talk or listen to a person who is draining your energy without reciprocating love, visualize yourself sitting under a glass dome. Their negative energy cannot reach you and you are sharing only the amount of time and energy that feels comfortable to you right now. After your encounter, wash your hands and stroke your wet hands over your body. From your shoulders to your hands, from chest to hips, from thighs to feet. Clear your energy field.

Make yourself a priority or you will not be able to be the best version of yourself next time. People who love and respect you and themselves will accept your boundaries.

SHIRSHASANA

CHANGE YOUR PERSPECTIVE

CHANGE YOUR LIFE

LOOK AT LIFE
WITH
GRATITUDE
INSTEAD
OF
EXPECTATIONS

I am in balance even if my life gets turned around. I blissfully accept all changes and obstacles I encounter on the journey of life.

None of us can complete this journey alone. We need each other. When we need a lesson or the universe thinks we are ready, a Guru shows up to lead us from the darkness of our mind into the light of our true Self, the soul. Anyone and anything can be a Guru, even a sickness or a painful event, so long as it puts us on the right track.

When I shift my point of view, I see a teaching in every life lesson and obstacle. I am understanding the messages the universe sends me and I accept them humbly.

Consciously use your memory now and look back to a life event that seemed horrible at the time. After much time has passed, do you see the lesson this event has taught you? Can you find gratitude and appreciation for what happened and seemed so wrong at the time?

Send out gratitude, bliss, and love to your Gurus, even if the lesson they taught you was a tough one. Send out gratitude to the virtuous people you have encountered in your life and let go of envy or jealousy. When giving advice on how to keep a serene mind, the sacred scriptures (Patanjali's Yoga Sutras) give us the following:

"By cultivating attitudes of friendliness toward the happy,

compassion for the unhappy,

delight for the virtuous,

and disregard toward the wicked,

the mind-stuff retains its undisturbed calmness."

Bring the tip of your thumb and middle finger together in Shuni Mudra. This hand position influences your energy flow to help you purify your mind and to transform negative thoughts into positive ones. The thumb represents the fire element and the middle finger ether. When those elements are imbalanced, we can experience anxiety or depression.

I am grateful for every lesson learned and invite life to be my teacher. I trust that the universe knows exactly what I need to learn and grow into the best version of myself.

I am here to serve as a human being and to contribute to the happiness and freedom of others. The world does not exist to make me happy, rather I exist for the world.

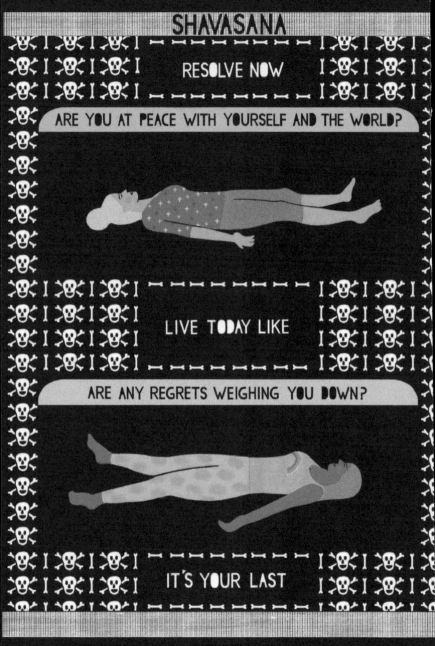

Relaxation teaches us the art of doing nothing. Of just being present. Of just being alive. It reminds us that we are enough. We have nothing to prove to ourselves or others, nor do we have to continuously strive for achievements.

Be conscious of your body's mortality—treat every moment as a precious gift because life can change or end in an instant. While you make plans, push yourself to achieve something, or try to change something that you have no business changing, you are missing out on life NOW.

I stop pushing myself. I just am.

I am comfortable doing nothing. I allow myself to do nothing. I am here now.

Get out of your head and start experiencing life with all five of your senses!

I am a human being . . . not a human doing!

I listen to my heart. I dream big. I do my best every day. I work hard. I believe in myself and my infinite possibilities and power. I leave the rest to the universe. I am not attached to a certain result. I trust that what is right will come.

(To a Yogi, death is like changing clothes or moving into a different house.)

MEDITATION

OF
DOING
NOTHING

All spiritual practices, as well as all Yoga postures and energy work, help us prepare our body and mind for meditation to happen. When the mind is clear and quiet, we are able to 'see' that which lies beyond our mind -- our true Self – just like when a lake is calm and still and the moon can 'see' its own reflection in the water below.

Meditation is doing and wanting nothing. Meditation is the opposite of our usual way of being in the world, when we compulsively follow our mind's desires, forget who we truly are, and forget that the mind is our instrument, which has to work FOR us and not against us.

Meditation is the state when nothing is missing, because that which is usually missing, resisting, or wanting, *is* the mind; when mediation happens, you experience what lies beyond the mind. You experience that which makes the mind think -- your true Self, energy, consciousness -- the part of you that is able to witness the movements of the mind, but is pure equanimity and free of duality. The part that can witness the boundaries and limits of the physical body, but itself is limitless.

That is the difference between creation (your body and mind) and the source of creation (your true Self). In nature or creation, everything is subject to time, space, change, duality, birth and death, day and night, good and bad. Everything always depends on something. As long as you are wrongly identified with your mind, your emotional state will always depend on something or someone. That is why you feel powerless.

Meditation means experiencing that which lies beyond the mind, your true SELF. That which had never been born and cannot die. That which is not subject to polarities, but is simply pure existence, equanimity, bliss, wisdom, and intelligence, and cannot and will never change. That which makes the mind think, the eyes see, the ears hear, the mouth speak, the heart beat, the wind blow, the sun rise....

Meditation is the state that cannot be explained with words, nor can it be taught. Words and scriptures can reach the mind and intellect, but never beyond. They can lead us on our path, but they are not enough to bring us there. Mediation and your true Self -- life itself -- can only be experienced through continuous, humble practice or the grace of an enlightened being.

You cannot "do" meditation. Meditation happens with God's grace when the time is right.

It is like falling asleep. You can prepare yourself and your environment and create a favorable atmosphere, but you cannot actively fall asleep; it just happens.

Most of what you know as meditation are techniques and practices that create a pleasant atmosphere in your energetic, mental, and physical bodies, which allow meditation to happen. You are practicing to still your mind, to just be. When you totally surrender your created identity, your thoughts, your opinions, and your desires and let go, you lay the ground for that indescribable experience— your way back home to your true Self. When you detach from your mind, there is no more darkness, only light.

You experience that you are not the mind that always wants something and you are not that body. You experience yourself as one with all existence. You experience a feeling of unconditional love and bliss. It is then that you understand life and life becomes joyful. You understand that there is no path to enlightenment, that enlightenment cannot be done, but that you have always been just that—light. You just weren't able to see it because you were wrongly identified with a human mind and a body.

When mediation happens with God's grace and after years of humble practice, you find all answers because your true Self is the intelligence of life, cosmic knowledge, unlimited wisdom. Limits and doubts, feelings of unknowing and incomprehension, exist only in the human mind. When you tap into your true Self -- the source of creation, that which animates all life forms – then, you know. You start to understand life. Everything makes sense. Everything starts communicating with you. Words are no longer needed, because they are the language of the mind. You simply feel, experience, and know.

Just be. Sit. Spine straight. Close your eyes. Focus on the third eye, the point between your eyebrows. Let your breath flow. Do nothing. Let your thoughts and sensations flow through you in the same way you allow your breath to flow through you. Do not interact with any thought or feeling. Just observe. Just listen. Do not enter into a dialogue with your mind. Do not wrap your attention around any thought. Let go. When your focus is entangled in your thoughts, notice it and let go. Focus on your breath. No expectations. Just be. No boredom. Just be. Be like a flower and just share your fragrance with life around you.

I am letting go. I let life happen.

GET OUT OF YOUR HEAD

FEEL THE SPARK +

AND INTO YOUR HEART

The content of your mind determines how you perceive life. You and your partner may experience the same situation or look at the same object but perceive it in a completely different way due to the contents specific to each of your minds.

Acknowledge that your partner has different beliefs and values, different feelings and thoughts, but beyond the chatter of the mind, you are both the same energy.

Your partner is living in a human form with a human mind and therefore has the same needs as you do (see Bakasana). Everybody gives priority to a different need and wants his or her needs to be satisfied in different ways. What might be right for you, might feel wrong for your partner.

No expectations, mutual respect, humor and communication are the keys to a harmonious relationship. Ask your partner what he/she needs more of and how exactly he/she wants this need to be satisfied.

I am connecting with my partner through my real Self.

I am moving beyond the differences of our minds and reaching into the unconditional love of our souls. We are all one.

CONCLUSION

You cannot control what happens in the external world, but you can control what happens in your mind.

There is already so much drama happening in the external world, which is why you want to make sure your inner world is pleasant and joyful.

Life just happens. How you experience life happens within you. What happens within you depends on the meaning you give to life events, circumstances, and other people's behavior.

For example, it rains. It is simply raining. If the rainy weather makes you sad and tired, or if you enjoy it with a cup of tea and a book, that happens within you. That is your choice. Life just happens. Feelings happen within you. They do not depend on life events, only on yourself—you always have the power to choose how you want to experience life.

It is YOUR mind and YOUR mind has to work FOR you.

Stop wasting your precious life time with worrying about things you cannot control or with complaining because life is not treating you as your mind believes it should. Life just happens! How you deal with it determines your experience of life and that's your responsibility.

HOW TO KEEP GOING

By internalizing and practicing *Yoga Coaching*'s teachings and tools, you will feel empowered to create a pleasant inner atmosphere in your body and mind. These simple yet powerful offerings will allow you to transcend the world of polarities and experience the underlying, ever-blissful essence of life as your true Self, a soul having a human experience in the game of life.

If you are curious and want to dive deeper into the layers of your being, learn more about Yoga philosophy and practices, mediation, and healing your heart, you will enjoy the book *Yoga Coaching*. Use your practice to resolve emotional baggage, master your mind, and create harmony in your life and relationship, or you can get in touch with Tina at www.tinastools.com.

ABOUT THE AUTHOR

Tina Mundelsee is a German national and has been working as a Spiritual Teacher, Yoga Therapist, and Life and Relationship Coach for more than fifteen years in seven different countries. Traveling the world, she understood that we are all motivated by the same desires, struggling with the same fears, and that the secret to leading a fulfilling life lies in finding the key to our mind and in remembering who we truly are. She has studied with the leaders in the coaching industry like Tony Robbins and has developed her knowledge about Yoga science, spirituality and intuitive abilities over many years under the guidance of her beloved Guruji from Paramanand University, India.

She is following her destiny of being a light worker and is helping others to let go of emotional baggage and limiting beliefs and to start believing again in the infinite possibilities and wonders of life. Tina is working online, teaching her clients from around the world how to create physical and mental balance, how to establish a pleasant atmosphere in their minds in order to live life joyfully and how to tune into higher realities of bliss and intelligence that lie beyond the limits of the human form.

ABOUT THE ILLUSTRATOR

Karen Abend is an artist and the founder of the Sketchbook Revival Online Workshop and Community. Originally from Southern California, she's been living in Sicily for over a decade.

After working in the field of art conservation in museums, archaeological excavations, international organizations, and universities, life led her in a different direction. She is grateful that she now gets to spend her time exploring her creative voice through personal and collaborative projects, while helping others to do the same.

Karen's art is driven by her love of creativity and the feeling of joy she receives from the creative process. This heart-centered approach infuses all of her creations, from greeting cards, to self-published books, and her sketchbook practice. Her ultimate goal is to create something every day and spread positive energy through the playful, vibrant, and uplifting imagery that comes out of her daily practice and other projects. Thanks to Tina for helping to make this possible.

www.karenabend.com

CPSIA information can be obtained
at www.ICGtesting.com
Printed in the USA
BVHW021437120722
641927BV00026B/1000